What a Wonderful World

igloobooks

Let's explore a brand-new day!
There's lots to hear and see,
from the smallest flower
to the very tallest tree.

This igloo book belongs to:

....

igloobooks

Published in 2021
First published in the UK by Igloo Books Ltd
An imprint of Igloo Books Ltd
Cottage Farm, NN6 0BJ, UK
Owned by Bonnier Books
Sveavägen 56, Stockholm, Sweden
www.igloobooks.com

0921 002
2 4 6 8 10 9 7 5 3
ISBN 978-1-80022-445-2

Written by Hannah Campling
Illustrated by Kathryn Inkson

Cover designed by Alex Alexandrou & Laura Chamberlain
Interiors designed by Alex Alexandrou
Edited by Hannah Campling

Printed and manufactured in China

Between the leafy branches,
the birds all flap and flitter.

They take flight from their nests, going

PEEP-PEEP,

CHIRP

and

TWITTER!

WHOOSH!

A breeze goes through the trees,
and whistles past your ear.

Sometimes it roars so loudly
that you can hardly hear!

Or it whispers softly,
a spell dancing all around...

... swooshing past with just
a very gentle **SHH-SHH** sound.

Do you hear that crackly
RUSTLE-RUSTLE everywhere?

That's the leaves high up above
you, swaying in the air.

When they turn from green to gold, they tumble, twirl and leap!

They scatter, spin in spirals and then pile up in a heap.

Little acorns fall among
the twisty forest roots.

With lots of rain and sunshine,
they appear as new green shoots.

Watch closely as
they start to grow!

Although they might
look small...

... these acorns
become oak trees,
with their branches
strong and tall.

Bees go **BUZZ** and **HUM** between
the sweetest smelling flowers.
They help keep gardens blooming.
Yes, bees have superpowers!

They zoom from plant to plant,
with sticky pollen on their feet.

This special job that bees do
gives us yummy food to eat.

It's lots of fun when raindrops
PITTER-PATTER from the sky.

You **SPLASH** around in puddles
as the rainbows arc up high.

The clouds begin
to clear and rain
glistens in the light.

Even after great big
storms, the sun will
soon shine bright.

In the sparkling river,
the water goes **SPLOSH-SPLISH!**

Peek past your reflection!
Can you see the swishing fish?

The hopping frogs go **CROAK!**

And the swans all swim and glide...

... while ducklings **QUACK** and **SQUELCH** on the muddy riverside.

The sky turns golden-yellow as the sun starts sinking low.
Crickets **CHIRP** in swishing grass and sleepy fireflies glow.

Evening is the time when all the world begins to rest.

Flower petals close
and squirrels snuggle
in their nests.

The day draws to an end,
and the fluffy owls **HOO-HOO!**

Stars are twinkling in the sky.
The moon shines brightly, too.

But the night is not as
still and quiet as it seems.

Badgers, bats and hedgehogs are
all waking from their dreams.

So, keep looking all around you. Play and jump and shout!
Search for magic every day. What will you find out?

You might discover something that you've never seen before.
The world is full of wonder and new beauty to explore!